# This journal belongs to:

- - - - - - - - - - - - - - - - - - - - - - - - -

# My star sign is:

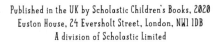

- - - - - - - - - - - - - - - - - - - - - - - - -

Published in the UK by Scholastic Children's Books, 2020
Euston House, 24 Eversholt Street, London, NW1 1DB
A division of Scholastic Limited

London ~ New York ~ Toronto ~ Sydney ~ Auckland
Mexico City ~ New Delhi ~ Hong Kong

SCHOLASTIC and associated logos are trademarks and/or
registered trademarks of Scholastic Inc.

Text by Laura Baker © Scholastic Children's Books
Designed by Cloud King Creative
Illustrations © Shutterstock

ISBN 978 07023 0343 2

A CIP catalogue record for this book is available from the British Library.

Printed and bound in China
Papers used by Scholastic Children's Books are made from wood grown in sustainable forests.

2 4 6 8 10 9 7 5 3 1

www.scholastic.co.uk

# My Astrology Journal

This astrology journal takes you through the year with the stars by your side. Discover your star sign, your ruling planet, your lucky day and more. There are crafts, activities and a magical recipe to try, too. Learn about each zodiac sign, then write your own star story, filling in your special memories under each sign.

## Let your star shine!

# Welcome to the cosmos!

Astrology is the interpretation of stars, planets and other celestial bodies: in particular, their movements in the sky and how these affect the universe – including you!

People all around the world have been studying different types of astrology for thousands of years. They find stories in the stars and pass them down through the generations. These stories are often about gods and goddesses, who rule different parts of the sky. Today, we call these stories 'mythology', and many of the planets are named after ancient gods and goddesses.

Astrologers believe that the movements of the stars, planets and moon in the sky can affect us in many different ways. They can even help us learn about our personalities, personal challenges and how we get on with others.

You can discover more about your cosmic portrait once you know your sun sign, or star sign. Your sun sign depends on the position of the sun in the sky when you were born.

Turn the page to begin your cosmic journey!

# You star!

What is your star sign? And what does it say about you? Read the pages that follow to help you fill in this cosmic profile **STARRING** you.

My name: ................................................................

My birthday: ..........................................................

My star sign: .........................................................

My ruling planet: ..................................................

My lucky day: .......................................................

My element:

Earth ☐  Air ☐  Water ☐  Fire ☐

# Three personality traits of my star sign that sound just like me:

1. _____

_____

2. _____

_____

3. _____

_____

# Two challenges of my star sign that sound just like me:

1. _____

_____

2. _____

_____

# The zodiac

The zodiac is a flat map of the sky, often laid out in a circle as if it were wrapped around the earth. It is divided into 12 sections. Each section was defined by a constellation found in that part of the sky, thousands of years ago. The 12 signs of the zodiac are: *Aries, Taurus, Gemini, Cancer, Leo, Virgo, Libra, Scorpio, Sagittarius, Capricorn, Aquarius* and *Pisces.*

Each sign has an element that goes with it,
representing different strengths.
The four elements are:

 **Fire** (action and passion)

 **Earth** (dependability and practicality)

 **Air** (ideas and communication)

 **Water** (emotion and empathy)

The zodiac is an astrologer's lens for viewing and
reading the universe. So where do you fit in?

# Read on!

# Capricorn

**Birthday:** 22nd December–19th January

**Symbol:** goat

**Ruling planet:** Saturn

**Element:** Earth

**Lucky day:** Saturday

If your birthday falls from **22nd December to 19th January, you are a Capricorn.**

**Capricorns** reach for the stars! They have big ambitions and will plan and work hard to achieve their goals. They can see the big picture and have incredible instincts to make it happen. They are brilliant at inspiring others to reach their full potential, too.

## Personality traits:

ambitious, driven, responsible, realistic, precise, determined, mature, strong leader

## Challenges:

★ **Capricorns** are so focused on the future that they can sometimes appear insensitive to others in the present.

★ **Capricorns** can work so hard that they forget to have fun. They need to find just the right balance.

★ **Capricorns** may see only the negative side of things. Remember to look at the positives too, Capricorn, and the world is yours!

# Putting plans in place

Capricorns are super driven and like to see
real results. Take a leaf from their book
and set some goals for the year ahead to
reach your own superstar status.

## Goal 1:

At school, I want to _ _ _ _ _ _ _ _ _ _ _ _ _ _ _ _ _ _ _ _ _ _ _ _ _ _ _ _ _

by _ _ _ _ _ _ _ _ _ _ _ _ _ _ _ _ _ _ _ _ _ _ _ _ _ _ _ _ _ _ _ _ _ (date).

I know I'll have reached my goal when I can _ _ _ _ _ _ _ _ _ _ _ _ _ _ _ _

_ _ _ _ _ _ _ _ _ _ _ _ _ _ _ _ _ _ _ _ _ _ _ _ _ _ _ _ _ _ _ _ _ _ _ _ _

Things I can do to help me reach my goal:

_ _ _ _ _ _ _ _ _ _ _ _ _ _ _ _ _ _ _ _ _ _ _ _ _ _ _ _ _ _

_ _ _ _ _ _ _ _ _ _ _ _ _ _ _ _ _ _ _ _ _ _ _ _ _ _ _ _ _ _

_ _ _ _ _ _ _ _ _ _ _ _ _ _ _ _ _ _ _ _ _ _ _ _ _ _ _ _ _ _

_ _ _ _ _ _ _ _ _ _ _ _ _ _ _ _ _ _ _ _ _ _ _ _ _ _ _ _ _ _

_ _ _ _ _ _ _ _ _ _ _ _ _ _ _ _ _ _ _ _ _ _ _ _ _ _ _ _ _ _

**Star tip:**
Remember that goals should
always be something that you
can realistically achieve by
a certain date. Make these
dreams that you can actually
reach – it will feel amazing
when you do!

## Goal 2:

At home, I want to _ _ _ _ _ _ _ _ _ _ _ _ _ _ _ _ _ _ _ _ _ _ _ _ _ _ _ _ _ _ _ _ _

by _ _ _ _ _ _ _ _ _ _ _ _ _ _ _ _ _ _ _ _ _ _ _ _ _ _ _ _ _ _ _ _ _ _ (date).

I know I'll have reached my goal when I can _ _ _ _ _ _ _ _ _ _ _ _ _ _ _ _

_ _ _ _ _ _ _ _ _ _ _ _ _ _ _ _ _ _ _ _ _ _ _ _ _ _ _ _ _ _ _ _ _ _ _ _ _ _ _ _ _ _ _

Things I can do to help me reach my goal: _ _ _ _ _ _ _ _ _ _ _ _ _ _ _

_ _ _ _ _ _ _ _ _ _ _ _ _ _ _ _ _ _ _ _ _ _ _ _ _ _ _ _ _ _ _ _ _ _ _ _ _ _ _ _ _ _ _

_ _ _ _ _ _ _ _ _ _ _ _ _ _ _ _ _ _ _ _ _ _ _ _ _ _ _ _ _ _ _ _ _ _ _ _ _ _ _ _ _ _ _

_ _ _ _ _ _ _ _ _ _ _ _ _ _ _ _ _ _ _ _ _ _ _ _ _ _ _ _ _ _ _ _ _ _ _ _ _ _ _ _ _ _ _

## Goal 3:

As a person, I want to _ _ _ _ _ _ _ _ _ _ _ _ _ _ _ _ _ _ _ _ _ _ _ _ _ _ _ _ _

by _ _ _ _ _ _ _ _ _ _ _ _ _ _ _ _ _ _ _ _ _ _ _ _ _ _ _ _ _ _ _ _ _ _ (date).

I know I'll have reached my goal when I can _ _ _ _ _ _ _ _ _ _ _ _ _ _ _ _

_ _ _ _ _ _ _ _ _ _ _ _ _ _ _ _ _ _ _ _ _ _ _ _ _ _ _ _ _ _ _ _ _ _ _ _ _ _ _ _ _ _ _

Things I can do to help me reach my goal: _ _ _ _ _ _ _ _ _ _ _ _ _ _ _

_ _ _ _ _ _ _ _ _ _ _ _ _ _ _ _ _ _ _ _ _ _ _ _ _ _ _ _ _ _ _ _ _ _ _ _ _ _ _ _ _ _ _

_ _ _ _ _ _ _ _ _ _ _ _ _ _ _ _ _ _ _ _ _ _ _ _ _ _ _ _ _ _ _ _ _ _ _ _ _ _ _ _ _ _ _

# My Capricorn diary

22nd December–19th January

What plans did you make under the
Capricorn sun this year? Write about
your achievements here.

22nd December–28th December _ _ _ _ _ _ _ _ _ _ _ _ _ _ _ _ _ _ _ _ _

_ _ _ _ _ _ _ _ _ _ _ _ _ _ _ _ _ _ _ _ _ _ _ _ _ _ _ _ _ _ _ _ _ _ _ _ _ _ _ _ _

_ _ _ _ _ _ _ _ _ _ _ _ _ _ _ _ _ _ _ _ _ _ _ _ _ _ _ _ _ _ _ _ _ _ _ _ _ _ _ _ _

_ _ _ _ _ _ _ _ _ _ _ _ _ _ _ _ _ _ _ _ _ _ _ _ _ _ _ _ _ _ _ _ _ _ _ _ _ _ _ _ _

29th December–4th January _ _ _ _ _ _ _ _ _ _ _ _ _ _ _ _ _ _ _ _ _ _ _

_ _ _ _ _ _ _ _ _ _ _ _ _ _ _ _ _ _ _ _ _ _ _ _ _ _ _ _ _ _ _ _ _ _ _ _ _ _ _ _ _

_ _ _ _ _ _ _ _ _ _ _ _ _ _ _ _ _ _ _ _ _ _ _ _ _ _ _ _ _ _ _ _ _ _ _ _ _ _ _ _ _

_ _ _ _ _ _ _ _ _ _ _ _ _ _ _ _ _ _ _ _ _ _ _ _ _ _ _ _ _ _ _ _ _ _ _ _ _ _ _ _ _

_ _ _ _ _ _ _ _ _ _ _ _ _ _ _ _ _ _ _ _ _ _ _ _ _ _ _ _ _ _ _ _ _ _ _ _ _ _ _ _ _

5th January–11th January _____

_____

_____

_____

_____

12th January–19th January _____

_____

_____

_____

_____

# Aquarius

**Birthday:** 20th January–18th February

**Symbol:** water carrier

**Ruling planet:** Uranus

**Element:** Air

**Lucky day:** Saturday

If your birthday falls from
20th January to 18th February, you are an Aquarius.
Aquarians will change the world. With a rebellious streak,
these free thinkers care deeply about the planet and will
do anything they can to protect it. They bring new and
original ideas to any cause they support and love
to make a difference.

## Personality traits:

humanitarian, independent, original, fresh, stubborn,

radical, rebellious, aloof

## Challenges:

★ While **Aquarians** are so focused on their cause, they can appear aloof to friends and family.

★ **Aquarians** need a positive place to focus their rebellious ideas.

★ They move to their own beat. Others may not understand, but you know you're going places, **Aquarius!**

# Be the change

Aquarians love to protect the world around them. What can you do to help your planet? Tick the suggestions you will try below. Then write your own planetary pledge.

## This year I will:

- [ ] try to walk, bike or scoot instead of making car journeys
- [ ] use reusable bags instead of plastic ones when shopping
- [ ] swap to bars of soap and bamboo toothbrushes to reduce throwaway plastic
- [ ] mend clothes instead of throwing them away
- [ ] have a clothes swap with friends to get a new look without buying new clothes
- [ ] turn off lights, devices and taps when not in use
- [ ] recycle and compost as much as possible

**Star tip:**
Get your family involved in trying these ideas, too!

## My planetary pledge

This year I promise to help my planet by:

**1.** ----------------------------------------------------------------

----------------------------------------------------------------

**2.** ----------------------------------------------------------------

----------------------------------------------------------------

**3.** ----------------------------------------------------------------

----------------------------------------------------------------

**4.** ----------------------------------------------------------------

----------------------------------------------------------------

**5.** ----------------------------------------------------------------

----------------------------------------------------------------

Signed: ----------------------------------------------------------------

Date: ----------------------------------------------------------------

# My Aquarius diary

### 20th January–18th February

What small changes did you make to help your planet? Record your excellent efforts here.

20th January–26th January _ _ _ _ _ _ _ _ _ _ _ _ _ _ _ _ _ _ _ _ _

_ _ _ _ _ _ _ _ _ _ _ _ _ _ _ _ _ _ _ _ _ _ _ _ _ _ _ _ _ _ _ _ _ _ _ _ _

_ _ _ _ _ _ _ _ _ _ _ _ _ _ _ _ _ _ _ _ _ _ _ _ _ _ _ _ _ _ _ _ _ _ _ _ _

_ _ _ _ _ _ _ _ _ _ _ _ _ _ _ _ _ _ _ _ _ _ _ _ _ _ _ _ _ _ _ _ _ _ _ _ _

_ _ _ _ _ _ _ _ _ _ _ _ _ _ _ _ _ _ _ _ _ _ _ _ _ _ _ _ _ _ _ _ _ _ _ _ _

27th January–2nd February _ _ _ _ _ _ _ _ _ _ _ _ _ _ _ _ _ _ _ _

_ _ _ _ _ _ _ _ _ _ _ _ _ _ _ _ _ _ _ _ _ _ _ _ _ _ _ _ _ _ _ _ _ _ _ _ _

_ _ _ _ _ _ _ _ _ _ _ _ _ _ _ _ _ _ _ _ _ _ _ _ _ _ _ _ _ _ _ _ _ _ _ _ _

_ _ _ _ _ _ _ _ _ _ _ _ _ _ _ _ _ _ _ _ _ _ _ _ _ _ _ _ _ _ _ _ _ _ _ _ _

_ _ _ _ _ _ _ _ _ _ _ _ _ _ _ _ _ _ _ _ _ _ _ _ _ _ _ _ _ _ _ _ _ _ _ _ _

3rd February–9th February _ _ _ _ _ _ _ _ _ _ _ _ _ _ _ _ _ _ _ _ _ _ _ _

_ _ _ _ _ _ _ _ _ _ _ _ _ _ _ _ _ _ _ _ _ _ _ _ _ _ _ _ _ _ _ _ _ _ _ _ _ _

_ _ _ _ _ _ _ _ _ _ _ _ _ _ _ _ _ _ _ _ _ _ _ _ _ _ _ _ _ _ _ _ _ _ _ _ _ _

_ _ _ _ _ _ _ _ _ _ _ _ _ _ _ _ _ _ _ _ _ _ _ _ _ _ _ _ _ _ _ _ _ _ _ _ _ _

_ _ _ _ _ _ _ _ _ _ _ _ _ _ _ _ _ _ _ _ _ _ _ _ _ _ _ _ _ _ _ _ _ _ _ _ _ _

10th February–18th February _ _ _ _ _ _ _ _ _ _ _ _ _ _ _ _ _ _ _ _ _ _

_ _ _ _ _ _ _ _ _ _ _ _ _ _ _ _ _ _ _ _ _ _ _ _ _ _ _ _ _ _ _ _ _ _ _ _ _ _

_ _ _ _ _ _ _ _ _ _ _ _ _ _ _ _ _ _ _ _ _ _ _ _ _ _ _ _ _ _ _ _ _ _ _ _ _ _

_ _ _ _ _ _ _ _ _ _ _ _ _ _ _ _ _ _ _ _ _ _ _ _ _ _ _ _ _ _ _ _ _ _ _ _ _ _

_ _ _ _ _ _ _ _ _ _ _ _ _ _ _ _ _ _ _ _ _ _ _ _ _ _ _ _ _ _ _ _ _ _ _ _ _ _

# Pisces

**Birthday:** 19th February–20th March

**Symbol:** fish

**Ruling planet:** Neptune

**Element:** Water

**Lucky day:** Thursday

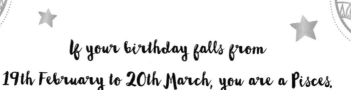

If your birthday falls from
19th February to 20th March, you are a Pisces.
Pisceans are so tuned in to other people's senses that
they're practically psychic! Highly sensitive and empathetic,
they also have hearts of gold. They are mystical and full
of daydreams and imagination. Their passion often leads
them to the creative arts.

## Personality traits:

sensitive, creative, artistic, dreamy, empathetic, spiritual, intuitive, detail-focused, impulsive

## Challenges:

★ **Pisceans** would rather live in the clouds than in reality!

★ **Pisceans** are highly sensitive and can get attached very easily. They need to find friends who will be there for them.

★ **Pisceans** may go along with others to avoid getting hurt. Believe in your superstar self, **Pisces!**

# Star Jar

**Dream like a Pisces!** Make a jar to hold all your hopes, dreams and inspirations. Then take them out each time you need a reminder of your cosmic potential.

**You will need:**
★ a large jar, with lid
★ coloured paper
★ scissors
★ glue

**1.** Choose a jar that's large enough to hold your notes, then carefully clean out and dry your jar.

**2.** Ask an adult to help you cut out star shapes from your coloured paper. Glue these around the outside of your jar.

**3.** Cut out the notes on the opposite page. Fold them, then pop them in your jar.

**4.** Over time, add more notes with your own words of wisdom, and your hopes and dreams.

*Take a note out to read it whenever you need a bit of dreamy inspiration!*

Shoot for the stars.

Something special is about to happen.

Believe in yourself.
Then others will believe in you too.

Never stop smiling.

Kindness is a superpower.

You are out-of-this-world wonderful.

Be brave. Be different. Be you.

Spread stardust wherever you go.

Every challenge helps you to grow.

Every mistake helps you to learn.

Hope never goes out of style.

Follow your dreams ... all the way to success.

# Mystical mindfulness

Take time to slow down and focus. Colour these
star patterns. Doodle your own stars, too.
Colour ... and breathe.

# My Pisces diary

19th February–20th March

What did you dream about under the **Pisces** sun? Catch your night-time dreams or day-time hopes below.

19th February–25th February _ _ _ _ _ _ _ _ _ _ _ _ _ _ _ _ _ _ _

_ _ _ _ _ _ _ _ _ _ _ _ _ _ _ _ _ _ _ _ _ _ _ _ _ _ _ _ _ _ _ _ _ _

_ _ _ _ _ _ _ _ _ _ _ _ _ _ _ _ _ _ _ _ _ _ _ _ _ _ _ _ _ _ _ _ _ _

_ _ _ _ _ _ _ _ _ _ _ _ _ _ _ _ _ _ _ _ _ _ _ _ _ _ _ _ _ _ _ _ _ _

26th February–3rd March _ _ _ _ _ _ _ _ _ _ _ _ _ _ _ _ _ _ _ _ _

_ _ _ _ _ _ _ _ _ _ _ _ _ _ _ _ _ _ _ _ _ _ _ _ _ _ _ _ _ _ _ _ _ _

_ _ _ _ _ _ _ _ _ _ _ _ _ _ _ _ _ _ _ _ _ _ _ _ _ _ _ _ _ _ _ _ _ _

_ _ _ _ _ _ _ _ _ _ _ _ _ _ _ _ _ _ _ _ _ _ _ _ _ _ _ _ _ _ _ _ _ _

4th March–10th March _ _ _ _ _ _ _ _ _ _ _ _ _ _ _ _ _ _ _ _ _ _ _ _ _

_ _ _ _ _ _ _ _ _ _ _ _ _ _ _ _ _ _ _ _ _ _ _ _ _ _ _ _ _ _ _ _ _ _ _ _ _

_ _ _ _ _ _ _ _ _ _ _ _ _ _ _ _ _ _ _ _ _ _ _ _ _ _ _ _ _ _ _ _ _ _ _ _ _

_ _ _ _ _ _ _ _ _ _ _ _ _ _ _ _ _ _ _ _ _ _ _ _ _ _ _ _ _ _ _ _ _ _ _ _ _

_ _ _ _ _ _ _ _ _ _ _ _ _ _ _ _ _ _ _ _ _ _ _ _ _ _ _ _ _ _ _ _ _ _ _ _ _


11th March–20th March _ _ _ _ _ _ _ _ _ _ _ _ _ _ _ _ _ _ _ _ _ _ _ _ _

_ _ _ _ _ _ _ _ _ _ _ _ _ _ _ _ _ _ _ _ _ _ _ _ _ _ _ _ _ _ _ _ _ _ _ _ _

_ _ _ _ _ _ _ _ _ _ _ _ _ _ _ _ _ _ _ _ _ _ _ _ _ _ _ _ _ _ _ _ _ _ _ _ _

_ _ _ _ _ _ _ _ _ _ _ _ _ _ _ _ _ _ _ _ _ _ _ _ _ _ _ _ _ _ _ _ _ _ _ _ _

_ _ _ _ _ _ _ _ _ _ _ _ _ _ _ _ _ _ _ _ _ _ _ _ _ _ _ _ _ _ _ _ _ _ _ _ _

# Aries

**Birthday:** 21st March–19th April

**Symbol:** ram

**Ruling planet:** Mars

**Element:** Fire

**Lucky day:** Tuesday

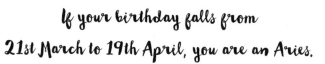

*If your birthday falls from*
*21st March to 19th April, you are an Aries.*
Being the first sign of the zodiac, **Aries** know how to get things started. **Aries** can be impulsive and enthusiastic, jumping straight in. They thrive on risk and the rush of excitement of new challenges. **Aries** are born leaders and like to take charge.

## Personality traits:

assertive, independent, competitive, courageous, energetic, spontaneous, passionate, honest, generous

## Challenges:

★ **Aries** move so fast that they can get bored easily!

★ **Aries** are very straightforward, so they may sometimes have trouble connecting with people who are less upfront.

★ **Aries** are miles ahead of everyone else and may need to wait for others to catch up.

★ Don't let them slow you down, **Aries** – hold on to your sense of self!

# Celestial symbols

Every star sign
has its own symbol.
Did you spot yours?

Most signs are people, animals or mythical creatures. The symbol for **Capricorn** is a sea-goat: a goat's body with the tail of a fish.

Every symbol has a meaning. For example, the **Pisces** symbol is two fish swimming in different directions. This shows that **Pisceans** are open to change and always moving.

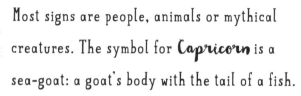

**Libra** is the only star sign that is not represented by an animal or a person. The scales show **Libra's** need for balance.

If you could create a new sign to suit you perfectly,
what would it be? Sketch your own celestial symbol below –
you could choose a mythical creature, an animal or something
that represents your best traits.

# My Aries diary

### 21st March–19th April

What did you do under the *Aries* sun this year?

Write your highlights of each week here.

21st–27th March _____

_____

_____

_____

_____

28th March–3rd April _____

_____

_____

_____

_____

4th–10th April _____

_____

_____

_____

_____

11th–19th April _____

_____

_____

_____

_____

# Taurus

**Birthday:** 20th April–20th May

**Symbol:** bull

**Ruling planet:** Venus

**Element:** Earth

**Lucky day:** Friday

*If your birthday falls from
20th April to 20th May, you are a Taurus.*
**Taurus** is the first of the Earth signs. **Taureans** are grounded, practical and ruled by their senses: touch, taste, sight, smell and hearing. They are kind to the planet and in sync with nature. They can be stubborn at times, but are devoted and loyal. A **Taurean** is a friend for life.

loyal, stubborn, determined, practical, resourceful,

cautious, methodical, sensible

## Challenges:

★ *Taureans* think practically. If they give advice to someone
who doesn't take practical steps to get out of a muddle,
*Taureans* can quickly become impatient!

★ *Taureans* don't like change and can be hesitant to leave
their comfort zone. They can sometimes think material
things are the most important thing in life.

★ Remember, *Taurus*, it's the star you are inside that counts!

# Galactic garden

## Love the earth like a Taurus!

You don't need loads of outdoor space to go green.
Try growing a garden on your window sill!

### You will need:

★ tin cans (carefully rinsed and dried)

★ herb seeds (from your local
garden centre or DIY shop)

★ felt-tip pens

★ thin card

★ PVA glue

★ potting soil

1. Collect your cans. You'll need one
for each different type of herb
you'd like to plant. You could
start with three and build
up to as many as will fit
on your window sill!

### Star tip:

Ask an adult to help
you in case of sharp
edges, then remove the
labels and carefully
rinse out the cans.

Thyme

Coriander

**2.** Cut out a card label for each of your cans. Write the name of the herb you will be planting on each one. Using strong PVA glue, stick a label on to each can. Leave to dry.

**3.** Place potting soil in each can, filling to about one centimetre below the rim.

**4.** Add several herb seeds to each can. Push the seeds down into the soil with your finger. Follow the instructions on the different herb packets for the best results.

**5.** Pour a little water into each can, allowing it to soak into the soil. Stop watering when water sits on top of the soil.

**6.** Place your herb cans on a sunny window sill. Remember to keep watering them regularly.

## Star tip:

These herbs aren't just pretty plants to admire – you can pick off leaves to use in all sorts of recipes. Remember to wash your herbs gently first!

# My Taurus diary

## 20th April–20th May

What challenges did you tackle under the
*Taurus* sun this year? Write your tests
and triumphs here.

20th–26th April _ _ _ _ _ _ _ _ _ _ _ _ _ _ _ _ _ _ _ _ _ _ _ _ _ _ _ _ _ _ _ _

_ _ _ _ _ _ _ _ _ _ _ _ _ _ _ _ _ _ _ _ _ _ _ _ _ _ _ _ _ _ _ _ _ _ _ _ _ _ _ _ _ _ _

_ _ _ _ _ _ _ _ _ _ _ _ _ _ _ _ _ _ _ _ _ _ _ _ _ _ _ _ _ _ _ _ _ _ _ _ _ _ _ _ _ _ _

_ _ _ _ _ _ _ _ _ _ _ _ _ _ _ _ _ _ _ _ _ _ _ _ _ _ _ _ _ _ _ _ _ _ _ _ _ _ _ _ _ _ _

27th April–3rd May _ _ _ _ _ _ _ _ _ _ _ _ _ _ _ _ _ _ _ _ _ _ _ _ _ _ _ _ _ _

_ _ _ _ _ _ _ _ _ _ _ _ _ _ _ _ _ _ _ _ _ _ _ _ _ _ _ _ _ _ _ _ _ _ _ _ _ _ _ _ _ _ _

_ _ _ _ _ _ _ _ _ _ _ _ _ _ _ _ _ _ _ _ _ _ _ _ _ _ _ _ _ _ _ _ _ _ _ _ _ _ _ _ _ _ _

_ _ _ _ _ _ _ _ _ _ _ _ _ _ _ _ _ _ _ _ _ _ _ _ _ _ _ _ _ _ _ _ _ _ _ _ _ _ _ _ _ _ _

_ _ _ _ _ _ _ _ _ _ _ _ _ _ _ _ _ _ _ _ _ _ _ _ _ _ _ _ _ _ _ _ _ _ _ _ _ _ _ _ _ _ _

4th May–10th May _____

_____

_____

_____

_____

11th May–20th May _____

_____

_____

_____

_____

# Gemini

**Birthday:** 21st May–20th June

**Symbol:** twins

**Ruling planet:** Mercury

**Element:** Air

**Lucky day:** Wednesday

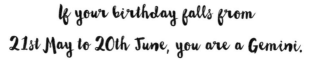

*If your birthday falls from
21st May to 20th June, you are a Gemini.*
Busy, busy, busy – **Geminis** are social creatures!
They are the life of the party, charming and playful.
Clever and curious, **Geminis** can pick things up quickly –
but they are so busy they'll most likely move on to the
next thing before others catch up!

## Personality traits:

curious, clever, restless, changeable, chatty, playful, silly, adaptable, unpredictable, adventurous

## Challenges:

★ **Geminis** are so sociable and chatty that they might not click with quieter signs. They need to find friends who can keep up!

★ Being interested in so many things, **Geminis** can sometimes appear unpredictable or uncommitted as they move to the next exciting thing.

★ **Geminis** can sometimes rush around so much that they can become frazzled and forgetful. Remember to slow down and find time for your awesome self, **Gemini**!

# Party planning

Channel social-butterfly *Gemini* and plan a party —
for a birthday, a special occasion or just because!
Choose a theme and then everything else to match.

- ☐ Unicorn dreamland
- ☐ Afternoon tea time
- ☐ Movie mania
- ☐ Trinket treasure hunt
- ☐ Other: _____

- ☐ Adventure in nature
- ☐ Karaoke sing-along
- ☐ Craft and create
- ☐ Sporting challenge

**Plan your menu.** What will you serve? Think about
drinks and food that match your theme.

_____

_____

_____

**Star tip:**
Get creative with your food design. For example, if you're having an astrology-themed party, you could cut each sandwich into the shape of a star or moon!

**Deck the halls.** Which decorations will you choose for your party? Jot down some ideas here. _ _ _ _ _ _ _ _ _ _ _ _ _ _ _ _ _ _

_ _ _ _ _ _ _ _ _ _ _ _ _ _ _ _ _ _ _ _ _ _ _ _ _ _ _ _ _ _ _ _ _ _

_ _ _ _ _ _ _ _ _ _ _ _ _ _ _ _ _ _ _ _ _ _ _ _ _ _ _ _ _ _ _ _ _ _

**Design your own invitation** or make copies of the invite on this page. Fill in the details and share with all your friends.

## You are invited to my party!

Date: _ _ _ _ _ _ _ _ _ _ _ _ _ _ _ _ _ _ _ _ _

Time: _ _ _ _ _ _ _ _ _ _ _ _ _ _ _ _ _ _ _ _ _

Place: _ _ _ _ _ _ _ _ _ _ _ _ _ _ _ _ _ _ _ _

RSVP to: _ _ _ _ _ _ _ _ _ _ _ _ _ _ _ _ _

# My Gemini diary

### 21st May–20th June

What activities did you get up to under
the *Gemini* sun? Did you try anything new?
Record them here.

21st–27th May _____

_____

_____

_____

28th May–3rd June _____

_____

_____

_____

_____

## Personality traits:

sensitive, family-oriented, caring, protective, thoughtful, nurturing, loyal, suspicious, worrisome

## Challenges:

★ **Cancers** can sometimes be a bit crabby – they are the crab, after all – but they are also very loving.

★ They can get cosy in their comfort zones and often retreat into their shells when they feel defensive or threatened. Once they feel safe, though, they'll be right there for you.

★ **Cancers** can, at times, become possessive of their close family and friends. Remember that sharing is caring!

# My family tree

Explore your family history like a caring Cancer.

## Grandparents

Name:

Birthday:

Star sign:

Name:

Birthday:

Star sign:

Name:

Birthday:

Star sign:

Name:

Birthday:

Star sign:

## Parents

Name:

Birthday:

Star sign:

Name:

Birthday:

Star sign:

**Siblings**

Name:

Birthday:

Star sign:

Name:

Birthday:

Star sign:

Name:

Birthday:

Star sign:

**Me**

Name:

Birthday:

Star sign:

Fill in the blanks above as best as you can – ask your family for help if needed. Do you think your family members are suited to their star signs?

# My Cancer diary

21st June–22nd July

Who did you connect with under the Cancer sun?
Record memorable meetings with family
and friends here.

21st June–27th June _ _ _ _ _ _ _ _ _ _ _ _ _ _ _ _ _ _ _ _ _ _ _ _ _

_ _ _ _ _ _ _ _ _ _ _ _ _ _ _ _ _ _ _ _ _ _ _ _ _ _ _ _ _ _ _ _ _ _ _

_ _ _ _ _ _ _ _ _ _ _ _ _ _ _ _ _ _ _ _ _ _ _ _ _ _ _ _ _ _ _ _ _ _ _

_ _ _ _ _ _ _ _ _ _ _ _ _ _ _ _ _ _ _ _ _ _ _ _ _ _ _ _ _ _ _ _ _ _ _

28th June–4th July _ _ _ _ _ _ _ _ _ _ _ _ _ _ _ _ _ _ _ _ _ _ _ _ _

_ _ _ _ _ _ _ _ _ _ _ _ _ _ _ _ _ _ _ _ _ _ _ _ _ _ _ _ _ _ _ _ _ _ _

_ _ _ _ _ _ _ _ _ _ _ _ _ _ _ _ _ _ _ _ _ _ _ _ _ _ _ _ _ _ _ _ _ _ _

_ _ _ _ _ _ _ _ _ _ _ _ _ _ _ _ _ _ _ _ _ _ _ _ _ _ _ _ _ _ _ _ _ _ _

5th July-11th July _ _ _ _ _ _ _ _ _ _ _ _ _ _ _ _ _ _ _ _ _ _ _ _ _ _
_ _ _ _ _ _ _ _ _ _ _ _ _ _ _ _ _ _ _ _ _ _ _ _ _ _ _ _ _ _ _ _ _ _ _ _
_ _ _ _ _ _ _ _ _ _ _ _ _ _ _ _ _ _ _ _ _ _ _ _ _ _ _ _ _ _ _ _ _ _ _ _
_ _ _ _ _ _ _ _ _ _ _ _ _ _ _ _ _ _ _ _ _ _ _ _ _ _ _ _ _ _ _ _ _ _ _ _
_ _ _ _ _ _ _ _ _ _ _ _ _ _ _ _ _ _ _ _ _ _ _ _ _ _ _ _ _ _ _ _ _ _ _ _

12th July-22nd July _ _ _ _ _ _ _ _ _ _ _ _ _ _ _ _ _ _ _ _ _ _ _ _ _
_ _ _ _ _ _ _ _ _ _ _ _ _ _ _ _ _ _ _ _ _ _ _ _ _ _ _ _ _ _ _ _ _ _ _ _
_ _ _ _ _ _ _ _ _ _ _ _ _ _ _ _ _ _ _ _ _ _ _ _ _ _ _ _ _ _ _ _ _ _ _ _
_ _ _ _ _ _ _ _ _ _ _ _ _ _ _ _ _ _ _ _ _ _ _ _ _ _ _ _ _ _ _ _ _ _ _ _
_ _ _ _ _ _ _ _ _ _ _ _ _ _ _ _ _ _ _ _ _ _ _ _ _ _ _ _ _ _ _ _ _ _ _ _

# Leo

**Birthday:** 23rd July–22nd August

**Symbol:** lion

**Ruling planet:** sun

**Element:** Fire

**Lucky day:** Sunday

If your birthday falls from
23rd July to 22nd August, you are a Leo.
Ruled by the sun and Fire, it's no surprise that Leos
are shining stars! These wildcats are natural performers
who love to shine in the limelight. Leos adore praise
but are also generous when working with others.
They are warm, fiercely loyal and strong.

## Personality traits:

optimistic, outgoing, passionate, showy, ambitious, friendly,

warm, brave, fierce, strong, proud, dramatic

## Challenges:

★ With their love of the spotlight, Leos can sometimes appear self-centred.

★ Leos know their worth, so they need to find friends who value them!

★ Leos don't always like to share the stage. Keep your jealousy at bay and you'll shine even brighter, Leo!

# Star shots

Look around you – you're surrounded by shining stars! Stick in pics or doodle your all-star cast of friends and family on these pages.

Funniest person I know

Most loyal friend ever

Most likely to discover a new planet

Most likely to
become prime
minister

Most likely to start
a new dance craze

Kindest
person in the
universe

Sweetest star
in the sky

# My Leo diary

### 23rd July–22nd August

## What shining moments did you have under the Leo sun? Write them down here.

23rd July–29th July _ _ _ _ _ _ _ _ _ _ _ _ _ _ _ _ _ _ _ _ _ _ _ _

_ _ _ _ _ _ _ _ _ _ _ _ _ _ _ _ _ _ _ _ _ _ _ _ _ _ _ _ _ _ _ _ _ _

_ _ _ _ _ _ _ _ _ _ _ _ _ _ _ _ _ _ _ _ _ _ _ _ _ _ _ _ _ _ _ _ _ _

_ _ _ _ _ _ _ _ _ _ _ _ _ _ _ _ _ _ _ _ _ _ _ _ _ _ _ _ _ _ _ _ _ _

_ _ _ _ _ _ _ _ _ _ _ _ _ _ _ _ _ _ _ _ _ _ _ _ _ _ _ _ _ _ _ _ _ _

30th July–5th August _ _ _ _ _ _ _ _ _ _ _ _ _ _ _ _ _ _ _ _ _ _ _

_ _ _ _ _ _ _ _ _ _ _ _ _ _ _ _ _ _ _ _ _ _ _ _ _ _ _ _ _ _ _ _ _ _

_ _ _ _ _ _ _ _ _ _ _ _ _ _ _ _ _ _ _ _ _ _ _ _ _ _ _ _ _ _ _ _ _ _

_ _ _ _ _ _ _ _ _ _ _ _ _ _ _ _ _ _ _ _ _ _ _ _ _ _ _ _ _ _ _ _ _ _

_ _ _ _ _ _ _ _ _ _ _ _ _ _ _ _ _ _ _ _ _ _ _ _ _ _ _ _ _ _ _ _ _ _

6th August–12th August _____

--------------------------------------------

--------------------------------------------

--------------------------------------------

--------------------------------------------

13th August–22nd August _____

--------------------------------------------

--------------------------------------------

--------------------------------------------

--------------------------------------------

# Virgo

**Birthday:** 23rd August–22nd September

**Symbol:** maiden

**Ruling planet:** Mercury

**Element:** Earth

**Lucky day:** Wednesday

*If your birthday falls from 23rd August to 22nd September, you are a Virgo.* Virgos just love to analyse and organize. Brilliant problem-solvers, they will study every detail to sort any problem in the cosmos. Quietly confident, **Virgos** are able to do almost anything they set their minds to. They are also extremely helpful and will always be there to support you.

## Personality traits:

perfectionist, smart, clever, practical, organized,
logical, helpful, thoughtful, quiet

## Challenges:

★ **Virgos'** love of detail can sometimes lead them to
overthink things, which can cause worries.

★ **Virgos** can feel shaken if their routine is disrupted.
They need to remember to breathe and give themselves
a break.

★ **Virgos** sometimes expect life to live up to the perfect
image they have in their head, while the reality doesn't
always match. Try to go with the flow, **Virgo!**

# My top fives

Uber-organized Virgo loves a list! Fill in your top fives to keep track of your picks of the moment.

My top five favourite films:

1. ----------------------------------------
2. ----------------------------------------
3. ----------------------------------------
4. ----------------------------------------
5. ----------------------------------------

My top five favourite people:

1. ----------------------------------------
2. ----------------------------------------
3. ----------------------------------------
4. ----------------------------------------
5. ----------------------------------------

Five things I want to do before the end of the year:

1. ----------------------------------------------
2. ----------------------------------------------
3. ----------------------------------------------
4. ----------------------------------------------
5. ----------------------------------------------

*Now think of a category of your own.*

My top five _____ :

1. ----------------------------------------------
2. ----------------------------------------------
3. ----------------------------------------------
4. ----------------------------------------------
5. ----------------------------------------------

# My Virgo diary

### 23rd August–22nd September

What were your biggest accomplishments under the Virgo sun? Did you do anything you're proud of at school or at home? Record your highs here.

23rd August–29th August _ _ _ _ _ _ _ _ _ _ _ _ _ _ _ _ _ _ _ _

_ _ _ _ _ _ _ _ _ _ _ _ _ _ _ _ _ _ _ _ _ _ _ _ _ _ _ _ _ _ _ _ _

_ _ _ _ _ _ _ _ _ _ _ _ _ _ _ _ _ _ _ _ _ _ _ _ _ _ _ _ _ _ _ _ _

_ _ _ _ _ _ _ _ _ _ _ _ _ _ _ _ _ _ _ _ _ _ _ _ _ _ _ _ _ _ _ _ _

30th August–5th September _ _ _ _ _ _ _ _ _ _ _ _ _ _ _ _ _ _ _ _

_ _ _ _ _ _ _ _ _ _ _ _ _ _ _ _ _ _ _ _ _ _ _ _ _ _ _ _ _ _ _ _ _

_ _ _ _ _ _ _ _ _ _ _ _ _ _ _ _ _ _ _ _ _ _ _ _ _ _ _ _ _ _ _ _ _

_ _ _ _ _ _ _ _ _ _ _ _ _ _ _ _ _ _ _ _ _ _ _ _ _ _ _ _ _ _ _ _ _

_ _ _ _ _ _ _ _ _ _ _ _ _ _ _ _ _ _ _ _ _ _ _ _ _ _ _ _ _ _ _ _ _

6th September–12th September _ _ _ _ _ _ _ _ _ _ _ _ _ _ _ _ _ _ _
_ _ _ _ _ _ _ _ _ _ _ _ _ _ _ _ _ _ _ _ _ _ _ _ _ _ _ _ _ _ _ _ _ _ _
_ _ _ _ _ _ _ _ _ _ _ _ _ _ _ _ _ _ _ _ _ _ _ _ _ _ _ _ _ _ _ _ _ _ _
_ _ _ _ _ _ _ _ _ _ _ _ _ _ _ _ _ _ _ _ _ _ _ _ _ _ _ _ _ _ _ _ _ _ _
_ _ _ _ _ _ _ _ _ _ _ _ _ _ _ _ _ _ _ _ _ _ _ _ _ _ _ _ _ _ _ _ _ _ _

13th September–22nd September _ _ _ _ _ _ _ _ _ _ _ _ _ _ _ _ _ _ _
_ _ _ _ _ _ _ _ _ _ _ _ _ _ _ _ _ _ _ _ _ _ _ _ _ _ _ _ _ _ _ _ _ _ _
_ _ _ _ _ _ _ _ _ _ _ _ _ _ _ _ _ _ _ _ _ _ _ _ _ _ _ _ _ _ _ _ _ _ _
_ _ _ _ _ _ _ _ _ _ _ _ _ _ _ _ _ _ _ _ _ _ _ _ _ _ _ _ _ _ _ _ _ _ _
_ _ _ _ _ _ _ _ _ _ _ _ _ _ _ _ _ _ _ _ _ _ _ _ _ _ _ _ _ _ _ _ _ _ _

# Libra

**Birthday:** 23rd September–22nd October

**Symbol:** scales

**Ruling planet:** Venus

**Element:** Air

**Lucky day:** Friday

*If your birthday falls from*
**23rd September to 22nd October, you are a Libra.**
Balance and harmony – it's what these scales were
made for! **Librans** love to find and create harmony
in people, situations and the world around them.
They often avoid conflict by not choosing a side.
All **Librans** want is a quiet life!

balanced, fair, diplomatic, impartial, mediating, charming, peaceful, agreeable, indecisive

## Challenges:

★ If a situation can't balance perfectly, Librans might find it hard to choose one side over another.

★ Librans can sometimes appear to be avoiding deeper issues, as they focus on creating lovely balance on the surface.

★ With their natural need to find peace, Librans can get drawn into other people's problems. Choose the causes that are important to you, Libra, to keep your own scales balanced!

# Perfect poetry

**Librans'** love of balance often leads them to the arts, where harmony can create beautiful things. Write a beautifully balanced acrostic poem, describing yourself using the letters of your star sign.

**What is an acrostic poem?** An acrostic poem starts with a vertical word, then uses each letter of that word to begin a line of the poem. For example:

**L** ovely

**I** ndecisive

**B** alanced

**R** esourceful

**A** ll they want is peace!

**Star tip:**
Each line can be a phrase or simply a word. It's up to you! You can even use a letter from the main word in the middle of a line if you get stuck.

## It's your turn! Craft your own cosmic acrostic.

Write your star sign in large letters vertically on the page.

Then write a poetic line for each letter, describing **you**!

- - - - - - - - - - - - - - - - - - - - - - - - - - - - - - - - - - - - -

- - - - - - - - - - - - - - - - - - - - - - - - - - - - - - - - - - - - -

- - - - - - - - - - - - - - - - - - - - - - - - - - - - - - - - - - - - -

- - - - - - - - - - - - - - - - - - - - - - - - - - - - - - - - - - - - -

- - - - - - - - - - - - - - - - - - - - - - - - - - - - - - - - - - - - -

- - - - - - - - - - - - - - - - - - - - - - - - - - - - - - - - - - - - -

- - - - - - - - - - - - - - - - - - - - - - - - - - - - - - - - - - - - -

- - - - - - - - - - - - - - - - - - - - - - - - - - - - - - - - - - - - -

- - - - - - - - - - - - - - - - - - - - - - - - - - - - - - - - - - - - -

- - - - - - - - - - - - - - - - - - - - - - - - - - - - - - - - - - - - -

# My Libra diary

### 23rd September–22nd October

How did you achieve harmony under the *Libra* sun
this year? Write the challenges you encountered
and your peaceful breakthroughs here.

23rd September–29th September _ _ _ _ _ _ _ _ _ _ _ _ _ _ _ _ _ _ _ _

_ _ _ _ _ _ _ _ _ _ _ _ _ _ _ _ _ _ _ _ _ _ _ _ _ _ _ _ _ _ _ _ _ _ _ _ _ _ _

_ _ _ _ _ _ _ _ _ _ _ _ _ _ _ _ _ _ _ _ _ _ _ _ _ _ _ _ _ _ _ _ _ _ _ _ _ _ _

_ _ _ _ _ _ _ _ _ _ _ _ _ _ _ _ _ _ _ _ _ _ _ _ _ _ _ _ _ _ _ _ _ _ _ _ _ _ _

30th September–5th October _ _ _ _ _ _ _ _ _ _ _ _ _ _ _ _ _ _ _ _ _

_ _ _ _ _ _ _ _ _ _ _ _ _ _ _ _ _ _ _ _ _ _ _ _ _ _ _ _ _ _ _ _ _ _ _ _ _ _ _

_ _ _ _ _ _ _ _ _ _ _ _ _ _ _ _ _ _ _ _ _ _ _ _ _ _ _ _ _ _ _ _ _ _ _ _ _ _ _

_ _ _ _ _ _ _ _ _ _ _ _ _ _ _ _ _ _ _ _ _ _ _ _ _ _ _ _ _ _ _ _ _ _ _ _ _ _ _

_ _ _ _ _ _ _ _ _ _ _ _ _ _ _ _ _ _ _ _ _ _ _ _ _ _ _ _ _ _ _ _ _ _ _ _ _ _ _

6th October–12th October _____

_____

_____

_____

_____


13th October–22nd October _____

_____

_____

_____

_____

# Scorpio

**Birthday:** 23rd October–21st November

**Symbol:** scorpion

**Ruling planet:** Pluto

**Element:** Water

**Lucky day:** Tuesday

*If your birthday falls from*
*23rd October to 21st November, you are a Scorpio.*
Dark, deep and mysterious, these scorpions may have a hard
exterior and a powerful sting, but they also have a softer side.
**Scorpios** love secrets – they'll dig deep to discover yours,
while guarding their own fiercely. If you prove you're worthy,
**Scorpios** will put their trust in you.

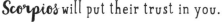

## Personality traits:

mysterious, deep, intense, secretive, powerful, ambitious, hardworking, dedicated, stubborn

## Challenges:

★ Though they appear tough, deep down **Scorpios** are not invincible and sometimes let their emotions get the better of them.

★ **Scorpios** can have trouble letting go and will hold a grudge to the end of the cosmos.

★ **Scorpios** can be wary of anyone they meet. Open yourself up to new friends, **Scorpio**, and you never know what you'll discover!

# Star biscuits

Make these gorgeously glittering star biscuits to share with your friends and family. Don't share the recipe, though – keep it your little secret, like a *Scorpio* would!

## You will need:

- ★ non-stick baking paper
- ★ 150 g butter
- ★ 75 g golden caster sugar
- ★ 2 tsp vanilla extract
- ★ 1 egg
- ★ 300 g flour
- ★ star-shaped cutter
- ★ 150 g white chocolate
- ★ gold and silver sprinkles

**1.** Ask an adult to pre-heat the oven to 180°C (160°C fan). Line two baking trays with non-stick baking paper.

**2.** Cream the butter, sugar and vanilla extract together in a mixing bowl until smooth. Add the egg and continue to mix, gradually adding the flour until you form a soft dough. Wrap in cling film and chill for 30 minutes.

**3.** Roll out the dough until it is ½ cm thick on a board dusted with a little flour. Cut out star shapes using a cutter. Place on the baking trays and bake for about 15 minutes until golden brown. Remove from the oven and cool on a wire rack.

**4.** Break up the chocolate and place in a heatproof bowl. Microwave on medium for one minute at a time, stirring the chocolate after each minute until it has melted.

**5.** To decorate, drizzle the chocolate over the top of the stars. Add the sprinkles, then leave to set.

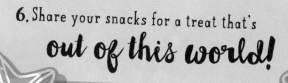

**6.** Share your snacks for a treat that's
*out of this world!*

# My Scorpio diary

### 23rd October–21st November

What secrets did you discover about yourself under the Scorpio sun? Write your revelations here.

23rd October–29th October _ _ _ _ _ _ _ _ _ _ _ _ _ _ _ _ _ _ _ _ _

_ _ _ _ _ _ _ _ _ _ _ _ _ _ _ _ _ _ _ _ _ _ _ _ _ _ _ _ _ _ _ _ _ _ _ _ _ _ _

_ _ _ _ _ _ _ _ _ _ _ _ _ _ _ _ _ _ _ _ _ _ _ _ _ _ _ _ _ _ _ _ _ _ _ _ _ _ _

_ _ _ _ _ _ _ _ _ _ _ _ _ _ _ _ _ _ _ _ _ _ _ _ _ _ _ _ _ _ _ _ _ _ _ _ _ _ _

_ _ _ _ _ _ _ _ _ _ _ _ _ _ _ _ _ _ _ _ _ _ _ _ _ _ _ _ _ _ _ _ _ _ _ _ _ _ _

30th October–5th November _ _ _ _ _ _ _ _ _ _ _ _ _ _ _ _ _ _ _ _ _

_ _ _ _ _ _ _ _ _ _ _ _ _ _ _ _ _ _ _ _ _ _ _ _ _ _ _ _ _ _ _ _ _ _ _ _ _ _ _

_ _ _ _ _ _ _ _ _ _ _ _ _ _ _ _ _ _ _ _ _ _ _ _ _ _ _ _ _ _ _ _ _ _ _ _ _ _ _

_ _ _ _ _ _ _ _ _ _ _ _ _ _ _ _ _ _ _ _ _ _ _ _ _ _ _ _ _ _ _ _ _ _ _ _ _ _ _

_ _ _ _ _ _ _ _ _ _ _ _ _ _ _ _ _ _ _ _ _ _ _ _ _ _ _ _ _ _ _ _ _ _ _ _ _ _ _

6th November-12th November _ _ _ _ _ _ _ _ _ _ _ _ _ _ _ _ _ _ _ _ _

_ _ _ _ _ _ _ _ _ _ _ _ _ _ _ _ _ _ _ _ _ _ _ _ _ _ _ _ _ _ _ _ _ _ _

_ _ _ _ _ _ _ _ _ _ _ _ _ _ _ _ _ _ _ _ _ _ _ _ _ _ _ _ _ _ _ _ _ _ _

_ _ _ _ _ _ _ _ _ _ _ _ _ _ _ _ _ _ _ _ _ _ _ _ _ _ _ _ _ _ _ _ _ _ _

_ _ _ _ _ _ _ _ _ _ _ _ _ _ _ _ _ _ _ _ _ _ _ _ _ _ _ _ _ _ _ _ _ _ _

13th November-21st November _ _ _ _ _ _ _ _ _ _ _ _ _ _ _ _ _ _ _ _

_ _ _ _ _ _ _ _ _ _ _ _ _ _ _ _ _ _ _ _ _ _ _ _ _ _ _ _ _ _ _ _ _ _ _

_ _ _ _ _ _ _ _ _ _ _ _ _ _ _ _ _ _ _ _ _ _ _ _ _ _ _ _ _ _ _ _ _ _ _

_ _ _ _ _ _ _ _ _ _ _ _ _ _ _ _ _ _ _ _ _ _ _ _ _ _ _ _ _ _ _ _ _ _ _

_ _ _ _ _ _ _ _ _ _ _ _ _ _ _ _ _ _ _ _ _ _ _ _ _ _ _ _ _ _ _ _ _ _ _

79

# Sagittarius

**Birthday:** 22nd November–21st December

**Symbol:** archer

**Ruling planet:** Jupiter

**Element:** Fire

**Lucky day:** Thursday

If your birthday falls from **22nd November**
to **21st December**, you are a **Sagittarius**.
**Sagittarians** are always looking for their next adventure.
Give them room to roam, and they'll go far! Exploring both
places and ideas, they've got serious energy and endless
excitement. They are honest and open with their friends,
telling things how they see them.

**Personality traits:**

adventurous, energetic, enthusiastic, independent,
positive, honest, clever, funny, impatient

**Challenges:**

★ With a **Sagittarius**, everything becomes bigger than it
started, and they can sometimes be known to exaggerate.

★ Super-honest **Sagittarians** need to be careful not to
offend their friends with their words.

★ **Sagittarians'** adventures can lead them in many
directions. Follow your passion, Sagittarius, and
you'll set the world on fire!

# Secret sign

Which star sign do you identify with?
Take this quiz to discover your secret sign.

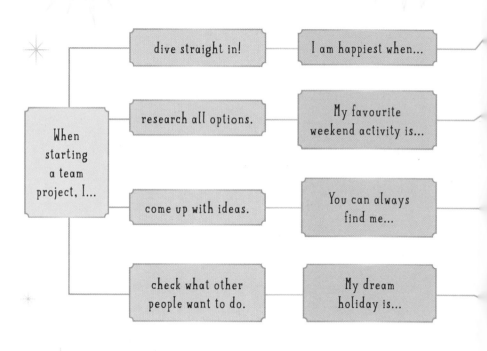

When starting a team project, I...

dive straight in!

research all options.

come up with ideas.

check what other people want to do.

I am happiest when...

My favourite weekend activity is...

You can always find me...

My dream holiday is...

| | |
|---|---|
| I am team captain. | *Aries* |
| I am performing on stage. | *Leo* |
| I am exploring somewhere new. | *Sagittarius* |
| reading a book. | *Virgo* |
| making a home movie. | *Capricorn* |
| tending to my garden. | *Taurus* |
| marching for a cause. | *Aquarius* |
| sorting out my friends' arguments. | *Libra* |
| at parties or after-school activities. | *Gemini* |
| a cosy cottage with my family. | *Cancer* |
| a cabin in the woods, with campfires and ghost stories! | *Scorpio* |
| a tropical beach where I can swim out to sea. | *Pisces* |

# My Sagittarius diary

## 22nd November–21st December

What adventures did you have under the
*Sagittarius* sun? Write down your memorable
moments – big or small – here.

22nd November–28th November _ _ _ _ _ _ _ _ _ _ _ _ _ _ _ _ _ _ _ _
_ _ _ _ _ _ _ _ _ _ _ _ _ _ _ _ _ _ _ _ _ _ _ _ _ _ _ _ _ _ _ _ _ _ _
_ _ _ _ _ _ _ _ _ _ _ _ _ _ _ _ _ _ _ _ _ _ _ _ _ _ _ _ _ _ _ _ _ _ _
_ _ _ _ _ _ _ _ _ _ _ _ _ _ _ _ _ _ _ _ _ _ _ _ _ _ _ _ _ _ _ _ _ _ _

29th November–6th December _ _ _ _ _ _ _ _ _ _ _ _ _ _ _ _ _ _ _ _
_ _ _ _ _ _ _ _ _ _ _ _ _ _ _ _ _ _ _ _ _ _ _ _ _ _ _ _ _ _ _ _ _ _ _
_ _ _ _ _ _ _ _ _ _ _ _ _ _ _ _ _ _ _ _ _ _ _ _ _ _ _ _ _ _ _ _ _ _ _
_ _ _ _ _ _ _ _ _ _ _ _ _ _ _ _ _ _ _ _ _ _ _ _ _ _ _ _ _ _ _ _ _ _ _
_ _ _ _ _ _ _ _ _ _ _ _ _ _ _ _ _ _ _ _ _ _ _ _ _ _ _ _ _ _ _ _ _ _ _

7th December–13th December _ _ _ _ _ _ _ _ _ _ _ _ _ _ _ _ _ _ _ _ _

_ _ _ _ _ _ _ _ _ _ _ _ _ _ _ _ _ _ _ _ _ _ _ _ _ _ _ _ _ _ _ _ _ _ _ _ _

_ _ _ _ _ _ _ _ _ _ _ _ _ _ _ _ _ _ _ _ _ _ _ _ _ _ _ _ _ _ _ _ _ _ _ _ _

_ _ _ _ _ _ _ _ _ _ _ _ _ _ _ _ _ _ _ _ _ _ _ _ _ _ _ _ _ _ _ _ _ _ _ _ _

_ _ _ _ _ _ _ _ _ _ _ _ _ _ _ _ _ _ _ _ _ _ _ _ _ _ _ _ _ _ _ _ _ _ _ _ _

14th December–21st December _ _ _ _ _ _ _ _ _ _ _ _ _ _ _ _ _ _ _ _

_ _ _ _ _ _ _ _ _ _ _ _ _ _ _ _ _ _ _ _ _ _ _ _ _ _ _ _ _ _ _ _ _ _ _ _ _

_ _ _ _ _ _ _ _ _ _ _ _ _ _ _ _ _ _ _ _ _ _ _ _ _ _ _ _ _ _ _ _ _ _ _ _ _

_ _ _ _ _ _ _ _ _ _ _ _ _ _ _ _ _ _ _ _ _ _ _ _ _ _ _ _ _ _ _ _ _ _ _ _ _

_ _ _ _ _ _ _ _ _ _ _ _ _ _ _ _ _ _ _ _ _ _ _ _ _ _ _ _ _ _ _ _ _ _ _ _ _

# The ruling planets

In astrology, each planet has its own energy and role. As the planets travel through the sky, they pass through the zodiac signs. Astrologers believe that the position of planets can influence your behaviour, hopes – and life!

**Sun**: truth, purpose, self-awareness

**Moon**: emotions, feelings, security

**Star tip:**
The sun and moon aren't actually planets, but in astrology, they are celestial bodies and give off energy like the planets do.

**Mercury**: communication, expression, reasoning

**Venus**: love, value, indulgence

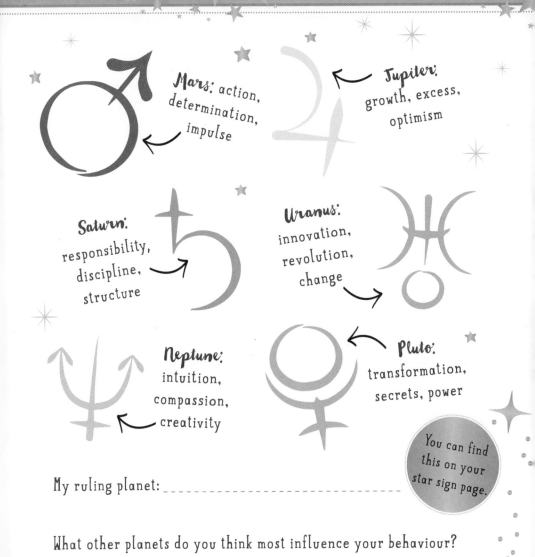

**Mars:** action, determination, impulse

**Jupiter:** growth, excess, optimism

**Saturn:** responsibility, discipline, structure

**Uranus:** innovation, revolution, change

**Neptune:** intuition, compassion, creativity

**Pluto:** transformation, secrets, power

You can find this on your star sign page.

My ruling planet: _ _ _ _ _ _ _ _ _ _ _ _ _ _ _ _ _ _ _ _ _ _ _ _ _ _ _

What other planets do you think most influence your behaviour?

_ _ _ _ _ _ _ _ _ _ _ _ _ _ _ _ _ _ _ _ _ _ _ _ _ _ _ _ _ _ _ _ _ _ _ _ _ _ _ _ _ _ _

# Mystical matches

The personality traits of some star signs complement each other well. These star signs are likely to be fast friends – a match made in the cosmos!

| | Your best friends: | | | | |
|---|---|---|---|---|---|
| | Capricorn | Aquarius | Pisces | Aries | Taurus |
| Capricorn | | | ★ | | ★ |
| Aquarius | | | | ★ | |
| Pisces | ★ | | | | ★ |
| Aries | | ★ | | | |
| Taurus | ★ | | ★ | | |
| Gemini | | ★ | | ★ | |
| Cancer | ★ | | ★ | | ★ |
| Leo | | ★ | | ★ | |
| Virgo | ★ | | ★ | | ★ |
| Libra | | ★ | | ★ | |
| Scorpio | ★ | | ★ | | ★ |
| Sagittarius | | ★ | | ★ | |

Your star sign:

See who you click with using this chart. Find your own star sign down the left side of the grid, then read across to discover your star sign compatibilities. For example, **Capricorn** is most compatible with **Pisces, Taurus, Cancer, Virgo** and **Scorpio**.

| Your best friends: | | | | | | |
|---|---|---|---|---|---|---|
| Gemini | Cancer | Leo | Virgo | Libra | Scorpio | Sagittarius |
|  | ★ |  | ★ |  | ★ |  |
| ★ |  | ★ |  | ★ |  | ★ |
|  | ★ |  | ★ |  | ★ |  |
| ★ |  | ★ |  | ★ |  | ★ |
|  | ★ |  | ★ |  | ★ |  |
|  | ★ |  |  | ★ |  | ★ |
|  |  |  | ★ |  | ★ |  |
| ★ |  |  |  | ★ |  | ★ |
|  | ★ |  |  |  | ★ |  |
| ★ |  | ★ |  |  |  | ★ |
|  | ★ |  | ★ |  |  |  |
| ★ |  | ★ |  | ★ |  |  |

# Phases of the moon

The moon goes through various phases as it travels around our planet. In astrology, each phase has its own energy. Note when you spot each of these phases in the sky.

**New Moon:** reflection, setting intentions

Date spotted: _ _ _ _ _ _ _ _ _ _ _ _ _ _ _ _ _ _

**Waxing Crescent:** breakthrough, taking action

Date spotted: _ _ _ _ _ _ _ _ _ _ _ _ _ _ _ _ _ _ _ _

**First Quarter:**

planning, organizing

Date spotted:

_ _ _ _ _ _ _ _ _ _ _ _ _

## Star tip:

Set your goals and intentions on the New Moon. Then see them develop through the moon's phases over the course of about 28 days.

**Waxing Gibbous**: questioning, perfecting

Date spotted: _ _ _ _ _ _ _ _ _ _ _ _ _ _ _ _ _ _ _ _ _ _ _ _ _

**Full Moon**: complete perspective,

discoveries, awareness

Date spotted: _ _ _ _ _ _ _ _ _ _ _ _ _ _ _ _ _ _ _ _ _ _ _ _

**Waning Gibbous**: connecting,

communicating, accomplishing

Date spotted: _ _ _ _ _ _ _ _ _ _ _ _ _ _ _ _ _ _ _ _

**Last Quarter**: seeing results

Date spotted: _ _ _ _ _ _ _ _ _ _ _ _ _ _ _ _ _ _ _ _ _ _

**Waning Crescent**: closure, reflection

Date spotted: _ _ _ _ _ _ _ _ _ _ _ _ _ _ _ _ _ _ _ _ _

# Looking back

That's a whole zodiac year over! What did you learn about yourself as you journeyed through the stars? Write your memories and ambitions here.

The top three things I achieved this year:

**1.** ---------------------------------------------------------------

**2.** ---------------------------------------------------------------

**3.** ---------------------------------------------------------------

Three things I would like to achieve next year:

**1.** ---------------------------------------------------------------

**2.** ---------------------------------------------------------------

**3.** ---------------------------------------------------------------

A new friend I made: ---------------------------------------------

Their star sign: -----------------------------------------------

Stick mementos on to this page:
ticket stubs, secret notes or even superstar selfies!